BY SUN AND CANDLELIGHT

Poetry and Prose for all Your Days

BY SUN AND CANDLELIGHT

This collection first published in 2010 by Hodder Children's Books
Selection copyright © Hodder Children's Books 2010
Illustrations copyright © Shirley Hughes 2010

Hodder Children's Books, 338 Euston Road, London, NW1 3BH
Hodder Children's Books Australia, Level 17/207 Kent Street, Sydney, NSW 2000

A catalogue record of this book is available from the British Library.

ISBN 978 0 340 98964 7
Printed in China

Hodder Children's Books is a division of
Hachette Children's Books,
an Hachette UK Company

www.hachette.co.uk

Note from the publisher: many poems are extracts only.
The title of the original poem is indicated at the
end of the book under list of extracts.

BY SUN AND CANDLELIGHT

Poetry and Prose for all Your Days

Illustrated by
Shirley Hughes

A division of Hachette Children's Books

Prologue

How do I love thee? Let me count the ways.
I love thee to the depth and breadth and height
My soul can reach, when feeling out of sight
For the ends of being and ideal grace.
I love thee to the level of every day's
Most quiet need, by sun and candle-light.
I love thee freely, as men strive for right.
I love thee purely, as they turn from praise.
I love thee with the passion put to use
In my old griefs, and with my childhood's faith.
I love thee with a love I seemed to lose
With my lost saints. I love thee with the breath,
Smiles, tears, of all my life; and, if God choose,
I shall but love thee better after death.

Elizabeth Barrett Browning

Foreward

Being asked to illustrate this collection was a thrilling challenge. It is not an anthology in the conventional sense, but a beautifully-wrought patchwork of extracts from poetry and prose, beginning with childhood rhymes and nonsense verse, on through adolescence, love and family and ending with eternity. It is rich in sentiment, but not in sentimentality. Some of it will open up new horizons to both older children and adults. Many of us will be sent happily back to re-read and re-discover forgotten pleasures.

I love illustrating in black and white line. It can combine sparkle and subtlety in all kinds of ways to enhance the page. The variety of material here, ranging from Tennyson and Jane Austen to Betjeman and Roger McGough, inspired great leaps of imagination and a huge range of characters. I very much hope that people will enjoy savouring and giving this book as much as I have enjoyed illustrating it.

Shirley Hughes

Contents

Chapter 1: When we were very young ★★★★★★★★★★★★★★★★★★★★11

Chapter 2: I think, therefore I am ★★★★★★★★★★★★★★★★★★★★★★27

Chapter 3: How do I love thee? ★★★★★★★★★★★★★★★★★★★★★★★★43

Chapter 4: We are family ★★★★★★★★★★★★★★★★★★★★★★★★★★★★★67

Chapter 5: You are old, father William ★★★★★★★★★★★★★★★★★★★81

Chapter 6: To sleep, perchance to dream ★★★★★★★★★★★★★★★★★91

List of extracts from poetry and prose★★★★★★★★★★★★★★★★★★106

Index of authors and poets ★★★★★★★★★★★★★★★★★★★★★★★★★★110

Acknowledgements ★★★★★★★★★★★★★★★★★★★★★★★★★★★★★★★112

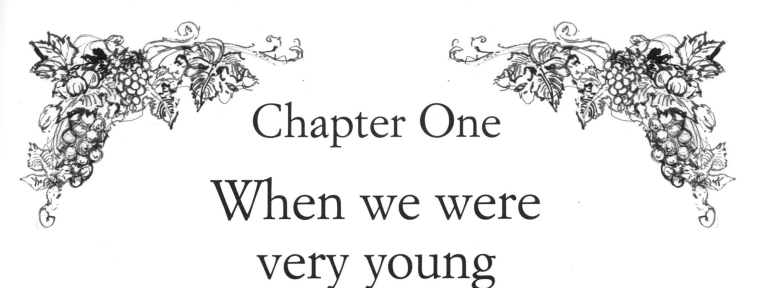

Chapter One
When we were very young

The Merchant of Venice

It is a wise father that knows his own child.
William Shakespeare

The Walrus and the Carpenter

The Walrus and the Carpenter
Walked on a mile or so,
And then they rested on a rock
Conveniently low:
And all the little Oysters stood
And waited in a row.

"The time has come," the Walrus said,
"To talk of many things:
Of shoes, and ships, and sealing-wax,
Of cabbages, and kings.
And why the sea is boiling hot
And whether pigs have wings."

Lewis Carroll

The Owl and the Pussycat

The Owl and the Pussycat went to sea
In a beautiful pea green boat,
They took some honey, and plenty of money,
Wrapped up in a five pound note.
The Owl looked up to the stars above,
And sang to a small guitar,
"O lovely Pussy! O Pussy my love,
What a beautiful Pussy you are,
You are,
You are!
What a beautiful Pussy you are!"

Edward Lear

The Quangle Wangle's Hat

On the top of the Crumpetty Tree
The Quangle Wangle sat,
But his face you could not see,
On account of his Beaver Hat.
For his hat was a hundred and two feet wide,
With ribbons and bibbons on every side
And bells, and buttons, and loops, and lace,
So that nobody ever could see the face
Of the Quangle Wangle Quee.

The Quangle Wangle said
To himself on the Crumpetty Tree,
"Jam; and jelly; and bread;
Are the best food for me!
But the longer I live on this Crumpetty Tree
The plainer than ever it seems to me
That very few people come this way

And that life on the whole is far from gay!"
Said the Quangle Wangle Quee.

Edward Lear

The Pobble who has no Toes

The Pobble who has no toes
Had once as many as we;
When they said, "Some day you may lose them all;"
He replied, "Fish fiddle de-dee!"
And his Aunt Jobiska made him drink
Lavender water tinged with pink,
For she said, "The world in general knows
There's nothing so good for a Pobble's toes!"

The Pobble who has no toes
Swam across the Bristol Channel;
But before he set out he wrapped his nose
In a piece of scarlet flannel.
For his Aunt Jobiska said, "No harm
Can come to his toes if his nose is warm;
And it's perfectly known that a Pobble's toes
Are safe – provided he minds his nose!"

Edward Lear

Know you what it is to be a child?… it is to believe in love, to believe in loveliness, to believe in belief; it is to be so little that the elves can reach to whisper in your ear; it is to turn pumpkins into coaches, and mice into horses, lowness into loftiness, and nothing into everything, for each child has its fairy godmother in its own soul.

Francis Thompson

The Mill on the Floss

We learn to restrain ourselves as we get older. We keep apart when we have quarrelled, express ourselves in well-bred phrases, and in this way preserve a dignified alienation, showing much firmness on one side, and swallowing much grief on the other. We no longer approximate in our behaviour to the mere impulsiveness of the lower animals, but conduct ourselves in every respect like members of a highly civilized society. Maggie and Tom were still very much like young animals, and so she could rub her cheek against his, and kiss his ear in a random sobbing way; and there were tender fibres in the lad that had been used to answer to Maggie's fondling, so that he behaved with a weakness quite inconsistent with his resolution to punish her as much as she deserved. He actually began to kiss her in return, and say,—

"Don't cry, then, Magsie; here, eat a bit o' cake."

Maggie's sobs began to subside, and she put out her mouth for the cake and bit a piece; and then Tom bit a piece, just for company, and they ate together and rubbed each other's cheeks and brows and noses together, while they ate, with a humiliating resemblance to two friendly ponies.

George Eliot

Wynken, Blynken and Nod

Wynken, Blynken, and Nod one night
Sailed off in a wooden shoe,
Sailed on a river of misty light
Into a sea of dew.
"Where are you going, and what do you wish?"
The old moon asked the three.
"We have come to fish for the herring fish
That live in this beautiful sea;
Nets of silver and gold have we,"
Said Wynken,
Blynken,
And Nod.

The old moon laughed and sang a song,

As they rocked in the wooden shoe;

And the wind that sped them all night long

Ruffled the waves of dew.

The little stars were the herring fish

That lived in the beautiful sea;

"Now cast your nets wherever you wish,

But never afeard are we!"

So cried the stars to the fishermen three:

Wynken,

Blynken,

And Nod.

Eugene Field

Shadow March

All around the house is the jet-black night;
It stares through the window-pane;
It crawls in the corners, hiding from the light,
And it moves with the moving flame.

Now my little heart goes a-beating like a drum,
With the breath of the Bogies in my hair;
And all around the candle the crooked shadows come,
And go marching along up the stair.

The shadow of the balusters, the shadow of the lamp,
The shadow of the child that goes to bed –
All the wicked shadows coming tramp, tramp, tramp,
With the black night overhead.

Robert Louis Stevenson

Timothy Winters

Timothy Winters comes to school
With eyes as wide as a football pool,
Ears like bombs and teeth like splinters:
A blitz of a boy is Timothy Winters.

His belly is white, his neck is dark,
And his hair is an exclamation mark.
His clothes are enough to scare a crow
And through his britches the blue winds blow.

When teacher talks he won't hear a word
And he shoots down dead the arithmetic-bird,
He licks the patterns off his plate
And he's not even heard of the Welfare State.

Timothy Winters has bloody feet

And he lives in a house on Suez Street,

He sleeps in a sack on the kitchen floor

And they say there aren't boys like him any more.

Old man Winters likes his beer

And his missus ran off with a bombadier,

Grandma sits in the grate with a gin

And Timothy's dosed with an aspirin.

The Welfare Worker lies awake

But the law's as tricky as a ten-foot snake,

So Timothy Winters drinks his cup

And slowly goes on growing up.

At Morning Prayers the Master helves
For children less fortunate than ourselves,
And the loudest response in the room is when
Timothy Winters roars "Amen!"

So come one angel, come on ten:
Timothy Winters says "Amen

Amen amen amen amen."
Timothy Winters, Lord. Amen.

Charles Causley

Chapter Two

I think, therefore I am

Hard Times

'Now what I want is, Facts. Teach these boys and girls nothing but Facts. Facts alone are wanted in life. Plant nothing else, and root out everything else… Stick to Facts, sir!'

Charles Dickens

Intentions: The Critic as Artist
With some remarks upon the importance of doing nothing

"Education is an admirable thing, but it is well to remember from time to time that nothing that is worth knowing can be taught."

Oscar Wilde

Little Women

If "genius is eternal patience," as Michelangelo affirms, Amy had some claim to the divine attribute, for she persevered in spite of all obstacles, failures, and discouragements, firmly believing that in time she would do something worthy to be called "high art".

Louisa May Alcott

Sonnet 94

They that have power to hurt and will do none,
That do not do the thing they most do show,
Who, moving others, are themselves as stone,
Unmoved, cold, and to temptation slow,
They rightly do inherit heaven's graces
And husband nature's riches from expense;
They are the lords and owners of their faces,
Others but stewards of their excellence.

The summer's flower is to the summer sweet,

Though to itself it only live and die,

But if that flower with base infection meet,

The basest weed outbraves his dignity:

For sweetest things turn sourest by their deeds;

Lilies that fester smell far worse than weeds.

William Shakespeare

A Song About Myself

There was a naughty boy,
And a naughty boy was he,
He ran away to Scotland
The people for to see –

There he found
That the ground
Was as hard,
That a yard
Was as long,
That a song
Was as merry,
That a cherry
Was as red,
That lead
Was as weighty,
That fourscore
Was as eighty,

That a door
Was as wooden
As in England –

So he stood in his shoes
And he wonder'd,
He wonder'd,
He stood in his
Shoes and he wonder'd.

John Keats

Growing Pains

The boy was barely five years old,
We sent him to the little school
And left him there to learn the names
Of flowers in jam jars on the sill
And learn to do as he was told.
He seemed quite happy there until
Three weeks afterwards, at night,
The darkness whimpered in his room.
I went upstairs, switched on his light,
And found him wide awake, distraught,
Sheets mangled and his eiderdown
Untidy carpet on the floor.
I said, "Why can't you sleep? A pain?"
He snuffled, gave a little moan,
And then he spoke a single word:
"Jessica." The sound was blurred.
"Jessica? What do you mean?"

"A girl at school called Jessica,
She hurts –" he touched himself between
The heart and stomach "– she has been
Aching here and I can see her."
Nothing I had read or heard
Instructed me in what to do.
I covered him and stroked his head.
"The pain will go in time," I said.

Vernon Scannell

Martin Chuzzlewit

He rose early next morning, and was a-foot soon after sunrise. But it was of no use; the whole place was up to see Mark Tapley off: the boys, the dogs, the children, the old men, the busy people and the idlers: there they were, all calling out "Good-by'e, Mark," after their own manner, and all sorry he was going. Somehow he had a kind of sense that his old mistress was peeping from her chamber-window, but he couldn't make up his mind to look back. "Good-by'e one, good-by'e all!" cried Mark, waving his hat on

the top of his walking-stick, as he strode at a quick pace up the little street. "Hearty chaps them wheelwrights – hurrah! Here's the butcher's dog a-coming out of the garden – down, old fellow! And Mr Pinch a-going to his organ – good-by'e, sir! And the terrier-bitch from over the way – hie, then, lass! And children enough to hand down human nature to the latest posterity – good-by'e, boys and girls! There's some credit in it now. I'm a-coming out strong at last. These are the circumstances that would try a ordinary mind; but I'm uncommon jolly. Not quite as jolly as I could wish to be, but very near. Good-by'e! good-by'e!"

Charles Dickens

Quest

Go south
Go north
Go east
Go west.
Still can't find God's address.

Go wake
Go dream
Go mountain
Go stream.
Still can't find God's address.

Go forest
Go city
Go church
Go charity.
Still can't find God's address.

It wasn't that God
Had moved out.
It was just that God
Had moved in –
That place called myself.

John Agard

Wuthering Heights

"I've no more business to marry Edgar Linton than I have to be in heaven; and if the wicked man in there had not bought Heathcliff so low, I shouldn't have thought of it. It would degrade me to marry Heathcliff now; so he shall never know how I love him: and that not because he's handsome, Nelly, but because he's more myself than I am. Whatever our souls are made of, his and mine are the same; and Linton's is as different as a moonbeam from lightning, or frost from fire."

Ere this speech ended, I became sensible of Heathcliff's presence. Having noticed a slight movement, I turned my head, and saw him rise from the bench and steal out noiselessly.

Emily Bronte

Be like the bird

Be like the bird, who
Resting in his flight
On a twig too slight
Feels it bend beneath him,
Yet sings
Knowing he has wings.

Victor Hugo

Chapter Three

How do I love thee?

The Lady of Shalott

Part 1

Four grey walls, and four grey towers,
Overlook a space of flowers,
And the silent isle imbowers
The Lady of Shalott.

By the margin, willow veil'd,
Slide the heavy barges trail'd
By slow horses; and unhail'd
The shallop flitteth silken-sail'd
Skimming down to Camelot:
But who hath seen her wave her hand?
Or at the casement seen her stand?
Or is she known in all the land,
The Lady of Shalott?

Only reapers, reaping early
In among the bearded barley,
Hear a song that echoes cheerly
From the river winding clearly,
Down to tower'd Camelot:
And by the moon the reaper weary,
Piling sheaves in uplands airy,
Listening whispers, "'Tis the fairy
Lady of Shalott."

Part 3

A bow-shot from her bower-eaves,

He rode between the barley sheaves,

The sun came dazzling thro' the leaves,

And flamed upon the brazen greaves

Of bold Sir Lancelot.

******

She left the web, she left the loom,

She made three paces through the room,

She saw the water-lily bloom,

She saw the helmet and the plume,

She look'd down to Camelot.

Out flew the web and floated wide;

The mirror crack'd from side to side;

"The curse is come upon me," cried

The Lady of Shalott.

Alfred, Lord Tennyson

The Highwayman

The wind was a torrent of darkness among the gusty trees,
The moon was a ghostly galleon tossed upon cloudy seas,
The road was a ribbon of moonlight, over the purple moor,
And the highwayman came riding –
Riding – riding –
The highwayman came riding, up to the old inn-door.

He'd a French cocked-hat on his forehead, a bunch of lace at his chin,
A coat of the claret velvet, and breeches of brown doe-skin;
They fitted with never a wrinkle: his boots were up to the thigh!
And he rode with a jewelled twinkle,
His pistol butts a-twinkle,
His rapier hilt a-twinkle, under the jewelled sky.
Over the cobbles he clattered and clashed in the dark inn-yard,
And he tapped with his whip on the shutters, but all was locked
and barred;

He whistled a tune to the window, and who should be waiting there

But the landlord's black-eyed daughter,

Bess, the landlord's daughter,

Plaiting a dark red love-knot into her long black hair.

Alfred Noyes

So We'll Go No More A-Roving

So, we'll go no more a-roving
So late into the night,
Though the heart be still as loving,
And the moon be still as bright.

For the sword outwears its sheath,
And the soul wears out the breast,
And the heart must pause to breathe
And love itself have rest.

Though the night was made for loving,
And the day returns too soon,
Yet we'll go no more a-roving
By the light of the moon.

George Gordon, Lord Byron

Far from the Madding Crowd

"Oh, how glad I am I came!" she exclaimed, thankfully, as she rose from her seat. "I have thought so much more of you since I fancied you did not want even to see me again. But I must be going now, or I shall be missed. Why Gabriel," she said, with a slight laugh, as they went to the door, "it seems exactly as if I had come courting you – how dreadful!"

"And quite right too," said Oak. "I've danced at your skittish heels, my beautiful Bathsheba, for many a long mile, and many a long day; and it is hard to begrudge me this one visit."

He accompanied her up the hill, explaining to her the details of his forthcoming tenure of the other farm. They spoke very little of their mutual feeling; pretty phrases and warm expressions being probably unnecessary between such tried friends. Theirs was that substantial affection which arises (if any arises at all) when the two who are thrown together begin first by knowing the rougher sides of each other's character, and not the best till further on, the romance growing up in the interstices of a mass of hard prosaic reality. This good-fellowship – camaraderie – usually occurring through similarity of pursuits, is unfortunately seldom superadded to love between the sexes, because men and women associate, not in their labours, but in their pleasures merely. Where, however, happy circumstance permits its development, the compounded feeling proves itself to be the only love which is strong as death – that love which many waters cannot quench, nor the floods drown, beside which the passion usually called by the name is evanescent as steam.

Thomas Hardy

The Raggle Taggle Gypsies

Three gypsies stood at the castle gate.
They sang so high, they sang so low.
My lady sate in her chamber late,
her heart it melted away as snow.

They sang so sweet, they sang so shrill,
that fast her tears began to flow,
And she lay down her silken gown,
her golden rings and all her show.

She took off her high-heeled shoes,
all made of Spanish leather-O,
She walked in the street in her bare, bare feet,
all out in the wind and weather-O.

"Saddle to me my milk white steed
and go and fetch me my pony-O.
So I may ride and seek my bride
who's gone with the raggle taggle gypsies-O!"

He rode high and he rode low,
he rode through woods and copses too,
Until he came to an open field
and there he espied his lady-O.

"What makes you leave your house and land,
your gold and treasure and all your show?
What makes you leave your new wedded lord,
to go with the raggle taggle gypsies-O?"

"What care I for my house and land?
What care I for my treasure-O?
What care I for my new-wedded lord?
I'm off with the raggle taggle gypsies-O!"

"Last night you slept on a goose-feather bed
with the sheet turned down so bravely-O.
Tonight you'll sleep in a cold, open field
along with the raggle taggle gypsies-O!"

"What care I for a goose-feather bed
with the sheet turned down so bravely-O?
Tonight I'll sleep in a cold, open field
along with the raggle taggle gypsies-O!"

Traditional

A Passionate Shepherd to his Love

Come live with me and be my Love,
And we will all the pleasures prove
That hills and valleys, dale and field,
And all the craggy mountains yield.

There will I make thee beds of roses
And a thousand fragrant posies,
A cap of flowers, and a kirtle
Embroider'd all with leaves of myrtle.

A belt of straw and ivy buds
With coral clasps and amber studs:
And if these pleasures may thee move,
Come live with me and be my Love.

Christopher Marlowe

Maud

Come into the garden, Maud,
For the black bat, night, has flown,
Come into the garden, Maud,
I am here at the gate alone;
And the woodbine spices are wafted abroad,
And the musk of the rose is blown.

Alfred, Lord Tennyson

Miss Joan Hunter Dunn
– A Subaltern's Love Song

Miss J. Hunter Dunn, Miss J. Hunter Dunn,
Furnish'd and burnish'd by Aldershot sun,
What strenuous singles we played after tea,
We in the tournament – you against me!
Love-thirty, love-forty, oh! weakness of joy,
The speed of a swallow, the grace of a boy,
With carefullest carelessness, gaily you won,
I am weak from your loveliness, Joan Hunter Dunn.

Miss Joan Hunter Dunn, Miss Joan Hunter Dunn,
How mad I am, sad I am, glad that you won,
The warm-handled racket is back in its press,
But my shock-headed victor, she loves me no less.

Her father's euonymus shines as we walk,
And swing past the summer-house, buried in talk,
And cool the verandah that welcomes us in
To the six-o'clock news and a lime-juice and gin.

The scent of the conifers, sound of the bath,
The view from my bedroom of moss-dappled path,
As I struggle with double-end evening tie,
For we dance at the Golf Club, my victor and I.

On the floor of her bedroom lie blazer and shorts,
And the cream-coloured walls are be-trophied with sports,
And westering, questioning settles the sun,
On your low-leaded window, Miss Joan Hunter Dunn.

The Hillman is waiting, the light's in the hall,
The pictures of Egypt are bright on the wall,
My sweet, I am standing beside the oak stair
And there on the landing's the light on your hair.

By roads "not adopted", by woodlanded ways,
She drove to the club in the late summer haze,
Into nine-o'clock Camberley, heavy with bells
And mushroomy, pine-woody, evergreen smells.

Miss Joan Hunter Dunn, Miss Joan Hunter Dunn,
I can hear from the car park the dance has begun,
Oh! Surrey twilight! importunate band!
Oh! strongly adorable tennis-girl's hand!

Around us are Rovers and Austins afar,
Above us the intimate roof of the car,
And here on my right is the girl of my choice,
With the tilt of her nose and the chime of her voice.

And the scent of her wrap, and the words never said,
And the ominous, ominous dancing ahead.
We sat in the car park till twenty to one
And now I'm engaged to Miss Joan Hunter Dunn.

John Betjeman

Good Morrow

I wonder, by my troth, what thou, and I
Did, till we lov'd? Were we not wean'd till then?
But suck'd on country pleasures, childishly?
Or snorted we in the seven sleepers' den?
'Twas so; but this, all pleasures fancies be.
If ever any beauty I did see,
Which I desir'd and got, 'twas but a dream of thee.

And now good morrow to our waking souls,
Which watch not one another out of fear;
For love, all love of other sights controls,
And makes one little room, an everywhere.
Let sea-discoverers to new worlds have gone,
Let Maps to other, worlds on worlds have shown,
Let us possess one world; each hath one, and is one.

John Donne

The Orange

At lunchtime I bought a huge orange –
The size of it made us all laugh.
I peeled it and shared it with Robert and Dave –
They got quarters and I had a half.

And that orange it made me so happy.
As ordinary things often do
Just lately. The shopping. A walk in the park.
This is peace and contentment. It's new.

The rest of the day was quite easy.
I did all the jobs on my list.
And enjoyed them and had some time over.
I love you. I'm glad I exist.

Wendy Cope

Chapter Four

We are family

I remember, I remember
The house where I was born,

Thomas Hood

The Railway Children

There were three of them. Roberta was the eldest. Of course, Mothers never have favourites, but if their Mother HAD had a favourite, it might have been Roberta. Next came Peter, who wished to be an Engineer when he grew up; and the youngest was Phyllis, who meant extremely well. Mother did not spend all her time in paying dull calls to dull ladies, and sitting dully at home waiting for dull ladies to pay calls to her. She was almost always there, ready to play with the children, and read to them, and help them to do their home-lessons. Besides this she used to write stories for them while they were at school, and read them aloud after tea, and she always made up funny pieces of poetry for their birthdays and for other great occasions, such as the christening of the new kittens, or the returning of the doll's house, or the time when they were getting over the mumps.

These three lucky children always had everything they needed: pretty clothes, good fires, a lovely nursery with heaps of toys, and a Mother Goose wall-paper. They had a kind and merry nursemaid, and a dog who was called James, and who was their very own. They also had a Father who was just perfect – never cross, never unjust, and always ready for a game – at least, if at any time he was NOT ready, he always had an excellent reason for it, and explained the reason to the children so interestingly and funnily that they felt sure he couldn't help himself.

E. Nesbit

Cinders

After the pantomime, carrying you back to the car
On the coldest night of the year
My coat, black leather, cracking in the wind.

Through the darkness we are guided by a star
It is the one the Good Fairy gave you
You clutch it tightly, your magic wand.

And I clutch you tightly for fear you blow away
For fear you grow up too soon and – suddenly,
I almost slip, so take it steady down the hill.

Hunched against the wind and hobbling
I could be mistaken for your grandfather
And sensing this, I hold you tighter still.

Knowing that I will never see you dressed for the Ball
Be on hand to warn you against Prince Charmings
And the happy ever afters of pantomime.

On reaching the car I put you into the baby seat
And fumble with straps I have yet to master
Thinking, if only there were more time. More time.

You are crying now. Where is your wand?
Oh no. I can't face going back for it
Let some kid find it in tomorrow's snow.

Waiting in the wings, the witching hour.
Already the car is changing. Smells sweet
Of ripening seed. We must go. Must go.

Roger McGough

The Quarrel

I quarrelled with my brother,
I don't know what about,
One thing led to another
And somehow we fell out.
The start of it was slight,
The end of it was strong,
He said he was right,
I knew he was wrong!
We hated one another.
The afternoon turned black.
Then suddenly my brother
Thumped me on the back,
And said, "Oh, come along!
We can't go on all night –
I was in the wrong."
So he was in the right.

Eleanor Farjeon

Love Me – I Love You

Love me – I love you,
Love me, my baby;
Sing it high, sing it low,
Sing it as may be.
Mother's arms under you,
Her eyes above you;
Sing it high, sing it low,
Love me – I love you.

Christina Rossetti

The Forsaken Merman

Come, dear children, let us away;
Down and away below.
Now my brothers call from the bay;
Now the great winds shoreward blow;
Now the salt tides seaward flow;
Now the wild white horses play,
Champ and chafe and toss in the spray.
Children dear, let us away.
This way, this way!

Call her once before you go.
Call once yet.
In a voice that she will know:
"Margaret! Margaret!"

Children's voices should be dear
(Call once more) to a mother's ear;
Children's voices, wild with pain.
Surely she will come again.
Call her once and come away.
This way, this way!
"Mother dear, we cannot stay."
The wild white horses foam and fret.
Margaret! Margaret!

Matthew Arnold

Pride and Prejudice

"An unhappy alternative is before you, Elizabeth. From this day forth you must be a stranger to one of your parents. Your mother will never see you again if you do not marry Mr Collins and I will never see you again if you do."

Jane Austen

The Iliad

The Trojan hero Hector is saying goodbye to his wife and his infant son before going into battle against the Greeks.

He stretched out his arms towards his child, but the boy cried and nestled against his nurse's bosom, scared at the sight of his father's armour, and at the horse hair plume that nodded fiercely from his helmet.

His father and mother laughed to see him, but Hector took his helmet from his head and laid it all gleaming upon the ground. Then he took his darling child, kissed him, and dandled him in his arms, praying over him the while to Jove and to all the gods.

Homer

Anna Karenina

All happy families are alike but an unhappy family is unhappy after its own fashion.

Leo Tolstoy

The Old Testament;
Second book of Samuel, 18

King David is at the gates of Jerusalem awaiting news of the battle and of his son, Absolom, who had rebelled against him.

And the King said unto Cushi, "is the young man Absolom safe?" And Cushi answered, "The enemies of my Lord the King, and all that arise against thee to do hurt, be as that young man is."
And the king was much moved, and went up to the chamber over the gate and wept: and as he wept, thus he said:
"O my son Absolom, my son, my son, Absolom!
Would that I had died for thee, O Absolom, my son, my son!"

Attrib. King Solomon

Gather ye Rosebuds

Gather ye rosebuds while ye may,
Old Time is still a-flying:
And this same flower that smiles today
Tomorrow will be dying.

Andrew Marvell

Chapter Five

You are old, father William

You are old, father William

"You are old, father William," the young man said,
"And your hair has become very white;
And yet you incessantly stand on your head –
Do you think, at your age, it is right?"

"In my youth," father William replied to his son,
"I feared it would injure the brain;
But now that I'm perfectly sure I have none,
Why, I do it again and again."

"You are old," said the youth, "as I mentioned before,
And have grown most uncommonly fat;
Yet you turned a back-somersault in at the door –
Pray, what is the reason of that?"

"In my youth," said the sage, as he shook his grey locks,
"I kept all my limbs very supple
By the use of this ointment – one shilling the box –
Allow me to sell you a couple."

"You are old," said the youth, "and your jaws are too weak
For anything tougher than suet;
Yet you finished the goose, with the bones and the beak –
Pray, how did you manage to do it?"

"In my youth," said his father, "I took to the law,
And argued each case with my wife;
And the muscular strength, which it gave to my jaw,
Has lasted the rest of my life."

"You are old," said the youth; "One would hardly suppose
That your eye was as steady as ever;
Yet you balanced an eel on the end of your nose –
What made you so awfully clever?"

"I have answered three questions, and that is enough,"
Said his father; "don't give yourself airs!
Do you think I can listen all day to such stuff?
Be off, or I'll kick you down stairs!"

Lewis Carroll

I used to Think…

I used to think that grown-up people chose
To have stiff backs and wrinkles round their nose,
And veins like small fat snakes on either hand,
On purpose to be grand.
Till through the banister I watched one day
My great-aunt Etty's friend who was going away,
And how her onyx beads had come unstrung.
I saw her grope to find them as they rolled;
And then I knew that she was helplessly old,
As I was helplessly young.

Frances Cornford

When You Are Old

When you are old and gray and full of sleep
And nodding by the fire, take down this book,
And slowly read, and dream of the soft look
Your eyes had once, and of their shadows deep;

How many loved your moments of glad grace,
And loved your beauty with love false or true;
But one man loved the pilgrim soul in you,
And loved the sorrows of your changing face.

And bending down beside the glowing bars,
Murmur, a little sadly, how Love fled
And paced upon the mountains overhead
And hid his face among a crowd of stars.

W.B. Yeats

Jenny Kiss'd Me

Jenny kiss'd me when we met
Jumping from the chair she sat in;
Time, you thief, who love to get
Sweets into your list, put that in!
Say I'm weary, say I'm sad,
Say that health and wealth have miss'd me,
Say I'm growing old, but add,
Jenny kiss'd me.

Leigh Hunt

Mrs Button

When Mrs Button, of a morning
        Comes creaking down the street,
You hear her old two black boots whisper
"Poor feet – poor feet – poor feet!"

When Mrs Button, every Monday,
    Sweeps the chapel neat;
All down the long, hushed aisles they whisper
"Poor feet – poor feet – poor feet!"

Mrs Button after dinner
(It is her Sunday treat)
Sits down and takes her two black boots off
And rests her two poor feet.

James Reeves

Wishes of an Elderly Man
Wished at a garden party, June 1914

I wish I loved the Human Race;
I wish I loved its silly face;
I wish I loved the way it walks;
I wish I liked the way it talks;
And when I'm introduced to one
I wish I thought What Jolly Fun!

Sir Walter Alexander Raleigh

Chapter Six

To sleep, perchance to dream

Hamlet

There are more things in heaven and earth, Horatio, than are dreamt of in your philosophy.

William Shakespeare

The Tempest

Full fathom five thy father lies,
Of his bones are coral made:
Those are pearls that were his eyes,
Nothing of him that doth fade,
But doth suffer a sea-change
Into something rich and strange.
Sea-Nymphs hourly ring his knell.
Hark! Now I hear them – ding-dong, bell.

William Shakespeare

Lights Out

I have come to the borders of sleep,
The unfathomable deep
Forest where all must lose
Their way, however straight,
Or winding, soon or late;
They cannot choose.

Edward Thomas

The Lady of Shalott

In the stormy east-wind straining,
The pale yellow woods were waning,
The broad stream in his banks complaining,
Heavily the low sky raining
Over tower'd Camelot;
Down she came and found a boat
Beneath a willow left afloat,
And round about the prow she wrote
The Lady of Shalott.

And down the river's dim expanse
Like some bold seer in a trance,
Seeing all his own mischance –
With a glassy countenance
Did she look to Camelot.
And at the closing of the day
She loosed the chain, and down she lay;
The broad stream bore her far away,
The Lady of Shalott.

Lying, robed in snowy white
That loosely flew to left and right –
The leaves upon her falling light –
Thro' the noises of the night
She floated down to Camelot:

And as the boat-head wound along
The willowy hills and fields among,
They heard her singing her last song,
The Lady of Shalott.

Heard a carol, mournful, holy,
Chanted loudly, chanted lowly,
Till her blood was frozen slowly,
And her eyes were darken'd wholly,
Turn'd to tower'd Camelot.
For ere she reach'd upon the tide
The first house by the water-side,
Singing in her song she died,
The Lady of Shalott.

Under tower and balcony,
By garden wall and gallery,
A gleaming shape she floated by,
Dead-pale between the houses high,
Silent into Camelot.

Out upon the wharfs they came,
Knight and burgher, lord and dame,
And round the prow they read her name,
The Lady of Shalott.

Who is this? and what is here?
And in the lighted palace near
Died the sound of royal cheer;
And they cross'd themselves for fear,
All the knights at Camelot:
But Lancelot mused a little space;
He said, "She has a lovely face;
God in his mercy lend her grace,
The Lady of Shalott."

Alfred, Lord Tennyson

The Old Testament
Ecclesiastes 3

To everything there is a season, and
a time to every purpose under heaven:
A time to be born, and
a time to die;
a time to plant, and
a time to pluck up
that which is planted;
****

A time to weep, and
a time to laugh;
a time to mourn, and
a time to dance;
****

A time to love, and
a time to hate;
a time of war; and
a time of peace.

The Bible attrib. King Solomon

The Walk

You did not walk with me
  Of late to the hill-top tree
By the gated ways,
As in earlier days;
You were weak and lame,
So you never came,
And I went alone, and I did not mind,
Not thinking of you as left behind.

I walked up there today
Just in the former way;
Surveyed around
The familiar ground
By myself again:
What difference, then?
Only that underlying sense
Of the look of a room on returning thence.

Thomas Hardy

Ozymandias

I met a traveller from an antique land
Who said: "Two vast and trunkless legs of stone
Stand in the desert. Near them on the sand,
Half sunk, a shattered visage lies, whose frown
And wrinkled lip and sneer of cold command
Tell that its sculptor well those passions read
Which yet survive, stamped on these lifeless things,
The hand that mocked them and the heart that fed.
And on the pedestal these words appear:
'My name is Ozymandias, King of Kings:
Look on my works, ye mighty, and despair!'
Nothing beside remains. Round the decay
Of that colossal wreck, boundless and bare,
The lone and level sands stretch far away."

Percy Bysshe Shelley

To His Coy Mistress

But at my back I always hear

Time's winged chariot hurrying near:

And yonder all before us lie

Deserts of vast eternity.

Thy beauty shall no more be found;

Nor, in the marble vault, shall sound

My echoing song: then worms shall try

That long-preserved virginity,

And your quaint honour turn to dust,

And into ashes all my lust.

The grave's a fine and private place,

But none, I think, do there embrace.

Andrew Marvell